G000166943

BOTANICAL
ADDRESS BOOK

ILLUSTRATED BY
GILLIAN BARLOW

LEOPARD

Personal Details

Name _____

Address _____

_____

Telephone (Home) _____ (Business) _____

National Insurance No. _____

Passport No. _____

Driving Licence No. _____

Bank Sort Code & Account No. _____

Address _____

Telephone _____

Doctor _____

Address _____

Telephone _____

Dentist _____

_____

Telephone _____

First published in Great Britain in 1995 by Leopard Books
Random House, 20 Vauxhall Bridge Road, London SW1V 2SA

Copyright © Random House UK Ltd 1995
All Illustrations © Gillian Barlow 1995

Whilst every effort has been made to ensure accuracy, the Publishers cannot accept liability for any errors

All rights reserved. No part of this book may be reproduced in any form or by any means without permission in writing from the publisher

Typeset in Copperplate Gothic by
SX Composing Ltd, Rayleigh, Essex
Printed and bound in Singapore

ISBN 0 7529 0090 0

Cover illustration: *Parrot Tulip*.

INTRODUCTION

THE ART OF BOTANICAL ILLUSTRATION, WHICH BEGAN IN EUROPE IN THE 15TH CENTURY, REACHED A PEAK OF ACHIEVEMENT IN THE 19TH WHEN SOME OF THE FINEST EXAMPLES WERE CREATED BY ARTISTS LIKE PIERRE JOSEPH REDOUTE. IT IS A BRANCH OF PAINTING CAPABLE OF PRODUCING RAVISHING WORKS OF ART, AND WHICH COMBINES SOME VERY SPECIAL SKILLS. THE FINEST EXAMPLES CAPTURE THE INHERENT BEAUTY OF THE FLOWERS THEMSELVES, AND SHOW AN UNDERSTANDING OF THE PLANT'S BOTANICAL CHARACTERISTICS. THEY ALSO SHOW A SENSE OF COMPOSITION AND DESIGN, AND GO BEYOND THE MERELY REPRESENTATIONAL TO PRODUCE PAINTINGS WHICH CAN MOVE AND DELIGHT US PROFOUNDLY.

THE GREAT AGE OF FLOWER PAINTING IN THE 18TH AND 19TH CENTURIES COINCIDED, FOR OBVIOUS REASONS, WITH A HUGE GROWTH OF INTEREST IN BOTANY IN GENERAL. AS TRAVEL THROUGHOUT THE WORLD BECAME LESS TROUBLESOME AND EXPENSIVE, PLANT-HUNTING EXPEDITIONS BROUGHT BACK SPECIMENS FROM EVERY CORNER OF THE GLOBE, BOTANICAL GARDENS WERE CREATED TO STUDY AND GROW THEM, AND BOTANICAL SCIENCE TOOK HUGE STRIDES FORWARDS. MANY OF THE PLANT-HUNTERS WERE IN A SENSE AMATEURS; AND MANY FINE FLOWER PAINTERS WERE EQUALLY UNINTERESTED IN EXPLOITING OR SELLING THEIR WORK.

TODAY, DESPITE CONSTANT REFINEMENT OF THE TECHNIQUE OF PLANT PHOTOGRAPHY, PAINTING IS OFTEN PREFERRED FOR SCIENTIFIC ILLUSTRATION. AN ARTIST CAN DISCRIMINATE BETWEEN IMPORTANT AND IRRELEVANT DETAIL MORE USEFULLY THAN THE CAMERA, AND CAN ALSO PRESENT THE INFORMATION IN A VISUALLY PLEASING WAY.

THERE ARE MANY FINE CONTEMPORARY BOTANICAL ARTISTS. THIS BOOK SHOWS THE RECENT WORK OF GILLIAN BARLOW WHO STUDIED PAINTING AT THE SLADE SCHOOL. SOME YEARS LATER SHE BEGAN PAINTING FLOWERS, BUILDING ON AN INTEREST AWAKENED BY HER BOTANIST FATHER, AND SOON DEVELOPED THIS MORE SERIOUSLY IN HER WORK. IN 1994 SHE WAS AWARDED THE ROYAL HORTICULTURAL SOCIETY'S GOLD MEDAL FOR BOTANICAL PAINTING, AND IS CURRENTLY WORKING FOR A SOLO EXHIBITION IN LONDON.

NAME

ADDRESS

PHONE   FAX

NAME

ADDRESS

PHONE   FAX

NAME

ADDRESS

PHONE   FAX

NAME

ADDRESS

PHONE   FAX

NAME

ADDRESS

PHONE   FAX

NAME

ADDRESS

PHONE   FAX

NAME

ADDRESS

PHONE   FAX

Rosa glauca

NAME

ADDRESS

PHONE   FAX

NAME

ADDRESS

PHONE   FAX

NAME

ADDRESS

PHONE   FAX

NAME

ADDRESS

PHONE   FAX

NAME

ADDRESS

PHONE   FAX

NAME

ADDRESS

PHONE   FAX

NAME

ADDRESS

PHONE   FAX

NAME

ADDRESS

PHONE   FAX

NAME

ADDRESS

PHONE   FAX

NAME

ADDRESS

PHONE   FAX

NAME

ADDRESS

PHONE   FAX

NAME

ADDRESS

PHONE   FAX

NAME

ADDRESS

PHONE   FAX

NAME

ADDRESS

PHONE   FAX

A

NAME

ADDRESS

PHONE   FAX

NAME

ADDRESS

PHONE   FAX

NAME

ADDRESS

PHONE   FAX

NAME

ADDRESS

PHONE   FAX

NAME

ADDRESS

PHONE   FAX

NAME

ADDRESS

PHONE   FAX

NAME

ADDRESS

PHONE   FAX

PASSION FLOWER

NAME

ADDRESS

PHONE   FAX

NAME

ADDRESS

PHONE   FAX

NAME

ADDRESS

PHONE   FAX

NAME

ADDRESS

PHONE   FAX

NAME

ADDRESS

PHONE   FAX

NAME

ADDRESS

PHONE   FAX

NAME

ADDRESS

PHONE   FAX

B

NAME

ADDRESS

PHONE   FAX

NAME

ADDRESS

PHONE   FAX

NAME

ADDRESS

PHONE   FAX

NAME

ADDRESS

PHONE   FAX

NAME

ADDRESS

PHONE   FAX

NAME

ADDRESS

PHONE   FAX

NAME

ADDRESS

PHONE   FAX

NAME

ADDRESS

PHONE   FAX

NAME

ADDRESS

PHONE   FAX

NAME

ADDRESS

PHONE   FAX

NAME

ADDRESS

PHONE   FAX

NAME

ADDRESS

PHONE   FAX

NAME

ADDRESS

PHONE   FAX

NAME

ADDRESS

PHONE   FAX

C

IRIS ENSATA

NAME

ADDRESS

PHONE   FAX

NAME

ADDRESS

PHONE   FAX

NAME

ADDRESS

PHONE   FAX

NAME

ADDRESS

PHONE   FAX

NAME

ADDRESS

PHONE   FAX

NAME

ADDRESS

PHONE   FAX

NAME

ADDRESS

PHONE   FAX

NAME

ADDRESS

PHONE   FAX

NAME

ADDRESS

PHONE   FAX

NAME

ADDRESS

PHONE   FAX

NAME

ADDRESS

PHONE   FAX

NAME

ADDRESS

PHONE   FAX

NAME

ADDRESS

PHONE   FAX

NAME

ADDRESS

PHONE   FAX

NAME

ADDRESS

PHONE   FAX

C

NAME

ADDRESS

PHONE   FAX

NAME

ADDRESS

PHONE   FAX

NAME

ADDRESS

PHONE   FAX

NAME

ADDRESS

PHONE   FAX

NAME

ADDRESS

PHONE   FAX

NAME

ADDRESS

PHONE   FAX

NAME

ADDRESS

PHONE   FAX

ROSA 'MARGUERITE HILLINGS'

NAME

ADDRESS

PHONE   FAX

NAME

ADDRESS

PHONE   FAX

NAME

ADDRESS

PHONE   FAX

NAME

ADDRESS

PHONE   FAX

NAME

ADDRESS

PHONE   FAX

NAME

ADDRESS

PHONE   FAX

NAME

ADDRESS

PHONE   FAX

NAME _____

ADDRESS _____

_____

PHONE _____ FAX _____

D

NAME _____

ADDRESS _____

_____

PHONE _____ FAX _____

NAME _____

ADDRESS _____

_____

PHONE _____ FAX _____

NAME _____

ADDRESS _____

_____

PHONE _____ FAX _____

NAME _____

ADDRESS _____

_____

PHONE _____ FAX _____

NAME _____

ADDRESS _____

_____

PHONE _____ FAX _____

NAME _____

ADDRESS _____

_____

PHONE _____ FAX _____

NAME

ADDRESS

PHONE   FAX

NAME

ADDRESS

PHONE   FAX

NAME

ADDRESS

PHONE   FAX

NAME

ADDRESS

PHONE   FAX

NAME

ADDRESS

PHONE   FAX

NAME

ADDRESS

PHONE   FAX

NAME

ADDRESS

PHONE   FAX

TULIPA TARDA

NAME

ADDRESS

PHONE   FAX

NAME

ADDRESS

PHONE   FAX

NAME

ADDRESS

PHONE   FAX

NAME

ADDRESS

PHONE   FAX

NAME

ADDRESS

PHONE   FAX

NAME

ADDRESS

PHONE   FAX

NAME

ADDRESS

PHONE   FAX

NAME

ADDRESS

PHONE   FAX

NAME

ADDRESS

PHONE   FAX

NAME

ADDRESS

HONE   FAX

NAME

ADDRESS

HONE   FAX

NAME

ADDRESS

HONE   FAX

NAME

ADDRESS

PHONE   FAX

NAME

ADDRESS

PHONE   FAX

E

NAME

ADDRESS

PHONE   FAX

NAME

ADDRESS

PHONE   FAX

NAME

ADDRESS

PHONE   FAX

NAME

ADDRESS

PHONE   FAX

NAME

ADDRESS

PHONE   FAX

NAME

ADDRESS

PHONE   FAX

NAME

ADDRESS

PHONE   FAX

ROSA MUNDI

NAME

ADDRESS

PHONE   FAX

NAME

ADDRESS

PHONE   FAX

NAME

ADDRESS

PHONE   FAX

NAME

ADDRESS

PHONE   FAX

NAME

ADDRESS

PHONE   FAX

NAME

ADDRESS

PHONE   FAX

NAME

ADDRESS

PHONE   FAX

NAME

ADDRESS

PHONE   FAX

NAME

ADDRESS

PHONE   FAX

F

NAME

ADDRESS

PHONE   FAX

NAME

ADDRESS

PHONE   FAX

NAME

ADDRESS

PHONE   FAX

NAME

ADDRESS

PHONE   FAX

NAME

ADDRESS

PHONE   FAX

NAME

ADDRESS

PHONE   FAX

NAME

ADDRESS

PHONE   FAX

NAME

ADDRESS

PHONE   FAX

NAME

ADDRESS

PHONE   FAX

NAME

ADDRESS

PHONE   FAX

NAME

ADDRESS

PHONE   FAX

NAME

ADDRESS

PHONE   FAX

IRIS SIBIRICA

NAME

ADDRESS

PHONE   FAX

NAME

ADDRESS

PHONE   FAX

NAME

ADDRESS

PHONE   FAX

NAME

ADDRESS

PHONE   FAX

NAME

ADDRESS

PHONE   FAX

NAME

ADDRESS

PHONE   FAX

NAME

ADDRESS

PHONE   FAX

NAME

ADDRESS

PHONE   FAX

NAME

ADDRESS

PHONE   FAX

G

NAME

ADDRESS

PHONE   FAX

NAME

ADDRESS

PHONE   FAX

NAME

ADDRESS

PHONE   FAX

NAME

ADDRESS

PHONE   FAX

NAME

ADDRESS

PHONE   FAX

NAME

ADDRESS

PHONE   FAX

NAME

ADDRESS

PHONE   FAX

NAME

ADDRESS

PHONE   FAX

NAME

ADDRESS

PHONE   FAX

NAME

ADDRESS

PHONE   FAX

NAME

ADDRESS

PHONE   FAX

NAME

ADDRESS

PHONE   FAX

ROSA MICRANTHA

NAME

ADDRESS

PHONE   FAX

NAME

ADDRESS

PHONE   FAX

NAME

ADDRESS

PHONE   FAX

NAME

ADDRESS

PHONE   FAX

NAME

ADDRESS

PHONE   FAX

NAME

ADDRESS

PHONE   FAX

NAME

ADDRESS

PHONE   FAX

NAME

ADDRESS

PHONE   FAX

NAME

ADDRESS

PHONE   FAX

H

NAME

ADDRESS

PHONE   FAX

NAME

ADDRESS

PHONE   FAX

NAME

ADDRESS

PHONE   FAX

NAME

ADDRESS

PHONE   FAX

NAME

ADDRESS

PHONE   FAX

NAME

ADDRESS

PHONE   FAX

NAME

ADDRESS

PHONE   FAX

NAME

ADDRESS

PHONE   FAX

NAME

ADDRESS

PHONE   FAX

NAME

ADDRESS

PHONE   FAX

NAME

ADDRESS

PHONE   FAX

NAME

ADDRESS

PHONE   FAX

Parrot tulip

NAME

ADDRESS

PHONE   FAX

NAME

ADDRESS

PHONE   FAX

NAME

ADDRESS

PHONE   FAX

NAME

ADDRESS

PHONE   FAX

NAME

ADDRESS

PHONE   FAX

NAME

ADDRESS

PHONE   FAX

NAME

ADDRESS

PHONE   FAX

NAME

ADDRESS

PHONE   FAX

NAME

ADDRESS

PHONE   FAX

NAME

ADDRESS

PHONE   FAX

NAME

ADDRESS

PHONE   FAX

NAME

ADDRESS

PHONE   FAX

NAME

ADDRESS

PHONE   FAX

NAME

ADDRESS

PHONE   FAX

I

NAME

ADDRESS

PHONE   FAX

NAME

ADDRESS

PHONE   FAX

NAME

ADDRESS

PHONE   FAX

NAME

ADDRESS

PHONE   FAX

NAME

ADDRESS

PHONE   FAX

NAME

ADDRESS

PHONE   FAX

NAME

ADDRESS

PHONE   FAX

Caltha palustris

NAME

ADDRESS

PHONE   FAX

NAME

ADDRESS

PHONE   FAX

NAME

ADDRESS

PHONE   FAX

NAME

ADDRESS

PHONE   FAX

NAME

ADDRESS

PHONE   FAX

NAME

ADDRESS

PHONE   FAX

NAME

ADDRESS

PHONE   FAX

NAME

ADDRESS

PHONE   FAX

NAME

ADDRESS

PHONE   FAX

NAME

ADDRESS

PHONE   FAX

NAME

ADDRESS

PHONE   FAX

NAME

ADDRESS

PHONE   FAX

NAME

ADDRESS

PHONE   FAX

NAME

ADDRESS

PHONE   FAX

J

NAME

ADDRESS

PHONE   FAX

NAME

ADDRESS

PHONE   FAX

NAME

ADDRESS

PHONE   FAX

NAME

ADDRESS

PHONE   FAX

NAME

ADDRESS

PHONE   FAX

NAME

ADDRESS

PHONE   FAX

NAME

ADDRESS

PHONE   FAX

ROSA 'QUEEN ELIZABETH'

NAME

ADDRESS

PHONE   FAX

NAME

ADDRESS

PHONE   FAX

NAME

ADDRESS

PHONE   FAX

NAME

ADDRESS

PHONE   FAX

NAME

ADDRESS

PHONE   FAX

NAME

ADDRESS

PHONE   FAX

NAME

ADDRESS

PHONE   FAX

NAME

ADDRESS

PHONE   FAX

NAME

ADDRESS

PHONE   FAX

NAME

ADDRESS

PHONE   FAX

K

NAME

ADDRESS

PHONE   FAX

NAME

ADDRESS

PHONE   FAX

NAME

ADDRESS

PHONE   FAX

NAME

ADDRESS

PHONE   FAX

NAME

ADDRESS

PHONE   FAX

NAME

ADDRESS

PHONE   FAX

NAME

ADDRESS

PHONE   FAX

NAME

ADDRESS

PHONE   FAX

NAME

ADDRESS

PHONE   FAX

NAME

ADDRESS

PHONE   FAX

NAME

ADDRESS

PHONE   FAX

HELLEBORUS FOETIDUS

NAME

ADDRESS

PHONE   FAX

NAME

ADDRESS

PHONE   FAX

NAME

ADDRESS

PHONE   FAX

NAME

ADDRESS

PHONE   FAX

NAME

ADDRESS

PHONE   FAX

NAME

ADDRESS

PHONE   FAX

NAME

ADDRESS

PHONE   FAX

NAME

ADDRESS

PHONE   FAX

NAME

ADDRESS

PHONE   FAX

NAME

ADDRESS

PHONE   FAX

NAME

ADDRESS

PHONE   FAX

L

NAME

ADDRESS

PHONE   FAX

NAME

ADDRESS

PHONE   FAX

NAME

ADDRESS

PHONE   FAX

NAME

ADDRESS

PHONE   FAX

NAME

ADDRESS

PHONE   FAX

NAME

ADDRESS

PHONE   FAX

NAME

ADDRESS

PHONE   FAX

NAME

ADDRESS

PHONE   FAX

NAME

ADDRESS

PHONE   FAX

NAME

ADDRESS

PHONE   FAX

ROSA SPINOSISSIMA

NAME

ADDRESS

PHONE   FAX

NAME

ADDRESS

PHONE   FAX

NAME

ADDRESS

PHONE   FAX

NAME

ADDRESS

PHONE   FAX

NAME

ADDRESS

PHONE   FAX

NAME

ADDRESS

PHONE   FAX

NAME

ADDRESS

PHONE   FAX

NAME

ADDRESS

PHONE   FAX

NAME

ADDRESS

PHONE   FAX

NAME

ADDRESS

PHONE   FAX

NAME

ADDRESS

M

PHONE   FAX

NAME

ADDRESS

PHONE   FAX

NAME

ADDRESS

PHONE   FAX

NAME

ADDRESS

PHONE   FAX

NAME

ADDRESS

PHONE   FAX

NAME

ADDRESS

PHONE   FAX

NAME

ADDRESS

PHONE   FAX

NAME

ADDRESS

PHONE   FAX

NAME

ADDRESS

PHONE   FAX

NAME

ADDRESS

PHONE   FAX

NAME

ADDRESS

PHONE   FAX

HELLEBORUS NIGER

NAME

ADDRESS

PHONE   FAX

NAME

ADDRESS

PHONE   FAX

NAME

ADDRESS

PHONE   FAX

NAME

ADDRESS

PHONE   FAX

NAME

ADDRESS

PHONE   FAX

NAME

ADDRESS

PHONE   FAX

NAME

ADDRESS

PHONE   FAX

NAME

ADDRESS

PHONE   FAX

NAME

ADDRESS

PHONE   FAX

NAME

ADDRESS

PHONE   FAX

NAME

ADDRESS

PHONE   FAX

N

NAME

ADDRESS

PHONE   FAX

NAME

ADDRESS

PHONE   FAX

NAME

ADDRESS

PHONE   FAX

NAME

ADDRESS

PHONE   FAX

NAME

ADDRESS

PHONE   FAX

NAME

ADDRESS

PHONE   FAX

NAME

ADDRESS

PHONE   FAX

NAME

ADDRESS

PHONE   FAX

NAME

ADDRESS

PHONE   FAX

NAME

ADDRESS

PHONE   FAX

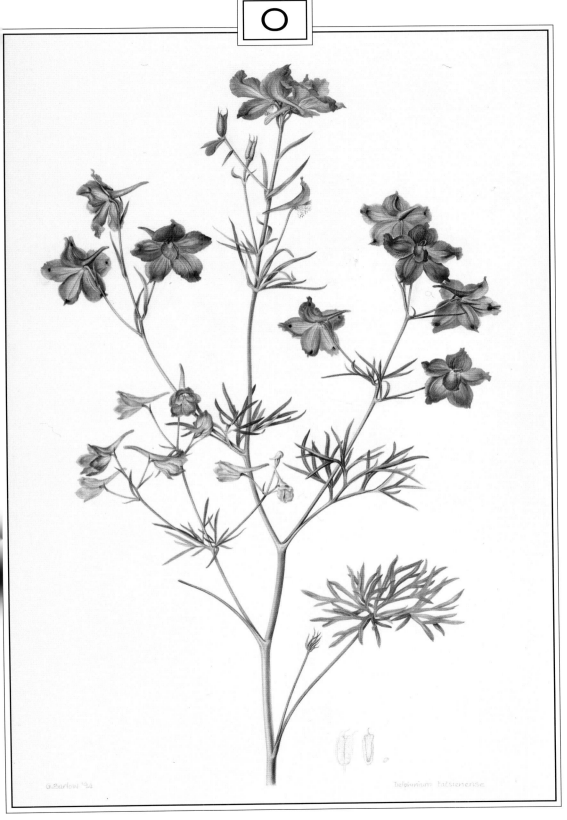

G.Barlow '94

Delphinium fatsienense

DELPHINIUM CHINENSIS

NAME

ADDRESS

PHONE   FAX

NAME

ADDRESS

PHONE   FAX

NAME

ADDRESS

PHONE   FAX

NAME

ADDRESS

PHONE   FAX

NAME

ADDRESS

PHONE   FAX

NAME

ADDRESS

PHONE   FAX

NAME

ADDRESS

PHONE   FAX

NAME _____

ADDRESS _____

_____

PHONE _____ FAX _____

NAME _____

ADDRESS _____

_____

PHONE _____ FAX _____

NAME _____

ADDRESS _____

_____

PHONE _____ FAX _____

NAME _____

ADDRESS _____

_____

PHONE _____ FAX _____

NAME _____

ADDRESS _____

_____

PHONE _____ FAX _____

NAME _____

ADDRESS _____

_____

PHONE _____ FAX _____

NAME _____

ADDRESS _____

_____

PHONE _____ FAX _____

NAME

ADDRESS

PHONE   FAX

NAME

ADDRESS

PHONE   FAX

NAME

ADDRESS

PHONE   FAX

NAME

ADDRESS

PHONE   FAX

NAME

ADDRESS

PHONE   FAX

NAME

ADDRESS

PHONE   FAX

NAME

ADDRESS

PHONE   FAX

ROSA MACROPHYLLA

NAME

ADDRESS

PHONE   FAX

NAME

ADDRESS

PHONE   FAX

NAME

ADDRESS

PHONE   FAX

NAME

ADDRESS

PHONE   FAX

NAME

ADDRESS

PHONE   FAX

NAME

ADDRESS

PHONE   FAX

NAME

ADDRESS

PHONE   FAX

NAME

ADDRESS

PHONE   FAX

NAME

ADDRESS

PHONE   FAX

NAME

ADDRESS

PHONE   FAX

NAME

ADDRESS

PHONE   FAX

NAME

ADDRESS

PHONE   FAX

P

NAME

ADDRESS

PHONE   FAX

NAME

ADDRESS

PHONE   FAX

NAME

ADDRESS

PHONE   FAX

NAME

ADDRESS

PHONE   FAX

NAME

ADDRESS

PHONE   FAX

NAME

ADDRESS

PHONE   FAX

NAME

ADDRESS

PHONE   FAX

NAME

ADDRESS

PHONE   FAX

NAME

ADDRESS

PHONE   FAX

Clematis viticella

Clematis viticella

NAME

ADDRESS

PHONE   FAX

NAME

ADDRESS

PHONE   FAX

NAME

ADDRESS

PHONE   FAX

NAME

ADDRESS

PHONE   FAX

NAME

ADDRESS

PHONE   FAX

NAME

ADDRESS

PHONE   FAX

NAME

ADDRESS

PHONE   FAX

NAME

ADDRESS

PHONE   FAX

NAME

ADDRESS

PHONE   FAX

NAME

ADDRESS

PHONE   FAX

NAME

ADDRESS

PHONE   FAX

NAME

ADDRESS

PHONE   FAX

Q

NAME

ADDRESS

PHONE   FAX

NAME

ADDRESS

PHONE   FAX

NAME

ADDRESS

PHONE   FAX

NAME

ADDRESS

PHONE   FAX

NAME

ADDRESS

PHONE   FAX

NAME

ADDRESS

PHONE   FAX

NAME

ADDRESS

PHONE   FAX

NAME

ADDRESS

PHONE   FAX

NAME

ADDRESS

PHONE   FAX

FRITILLARIA MELEAGRIS

NAME

ADDRESS

PHONE   FAX

NAME

ADDRESS

PHONE   FAX

NAME

ADDRESS

PHONE   FAX

NAME

ADDRESS

PHONE   FAX

NAME

ADDRESS

PHONE   FAX

NAME

ADDRESS

PHONE   FAX

NAME

ADDRESS

PHONE   FAX

NAME

ADDRESS

PHONE   FAX

NAME

ADDRESS

PHONE   FAX

NAME

ADDRESS

PHONE   FAX

NAME

ADDRESS

PHONE   FAX

NAME

ADDRESS

PHONE   FAX

NAME

ADDRESS

PHONE   FAX

NAME

ADDRESS

PHONE   FAX

R

NAME

ADDRESS

PHONE   FAX

NAME

ADDRESS

PHONE   FAX

NAME

ADDRESS

PHONE   FAX

NAME

ADDRESS

PHONE   FAX

NAME

ADDRESS

PHONE   FAX

NAME

ADDRESS

PHONE   FAX

NAME

ADDRESS

PHONE   FAX

SUTHERLANDIA

NAME

ADDRESS

PHONE   FAX

NAME

ADDRESS

PHONE   FAX

NAME

ADDRESS

PHONE   FAX

NAME

ADDRESS

PHONE   FAX

NAME

ADDRESS

PHONE   FAX

NAME

ADDRESS

PHONE   FAX

NAME

ADDRESS

PHONE   FAX

NAME

ADDRESS

PHONE   FAX

NAME

ADDRESS

PHONE   FAX

NAME

ADDRESS

PHONE   FAX

NAME

ADDRESS

PHONE   FAX

NAME

ADDRESS

PHONE   FAX

NAME

ADDRESS

PHONE   FAX

NAME

ADDRESS

PHONE   FAX

S

NAME

ADDRESS

PHONE   FAX

NAME

ADDRESS

PHONE   FAX

NAME

ADDRESS

PHONE   FAX

NAME

ADDRESS

PHONE   FAX

NAME

ADDRESS

PHONE   FAX

NAME

ADDRESS

PHONE   FAX

NAME

ADDRESS

PHONE   FAX

Corydalis flexuosa

NAME

ADDRESS

PHONE   FAX

NAME

ADDRESS

PHONE   FAX

NAME

ADDRESS

PHONE   FAX

NAME

ADDRESS

PHONE   FAX

NAME

ADDRESS

PHONE   FAX

NAME

ADDRESS

PHONE   FAX

NAME

ADDRESS

PHONE   FAX

NAME

ADDRESS

PHONE   FAX

NAME

ADDRESS

PHONE   FAX

NAME

ADDRESS

PHONE   FAX

NAME

ADDRESS

PHONE   FAX

NAME

ADDRESS

PHONE   FAX

NAME

ADDRESS

PHONE   FAX

NAME

ADDRESS

PHONE   FAX

T

NAME

ADDRESS

PHONE   FAX

NAME

ADDRESS

PHONE   FAX

NAME

ADDRESS

PHONE   FAX

NAME

ADDRESS

PHONE   FAX

NAME

ADDRESS

PHONE   FAX

NAME

ADDRESS

PHONE   FAX

NAME

ADDRESS

PHONE   FAX

HIPPEASTRUM

NAME

ADDRESS

PHONE   FAX

NAME

ADDRESS

PHONE   FAX

NAME

ADDRESS

PHONE   FAX

NAME

ADDRESS

PHONE   FAX

NAME

ADDRESS

PHONE   FAX

NAME

ADDRESS

PHONE   FAX

NAME

ADDRESS

PHONE   FAX

NAME _____

ADDRESS _____

_____

PHONE _____ FAX _____

NAME _____

ADDRESS _____

_____

PHONE _____ FAX _____

NAME _____

ADDRESS _____

_____

PHONE _____ FAX _____

NAME _____

ADDRESS _____

_____

PHONE _____ FAX _____

NAME _____

ADDRESS _____

_____

PHONE _____ FAX _____

NAME _____

ADDRESS _____

_____

PHONE _____ FAX _____

U

NAME _____

ADDRESS _____

_____

PHONE _____ FAX _____

NAME

ADDRESS

PHONE   FAX

NAME

ADDRESS

PHONE   FAX

NAME

ADDRESS

PHONE   FAX

NAME

ADDRESS

PHONE   FAX

NAME

ADDRESS

PHONE   FAX

NAME

ADDRESS

PHONE   FAX

NAME

ADDRESS

PHONE   FAX

NICOTIANA

NAME

ADDRESS

PHONE   FAX

NAME

ADDRESS

PHONE   FAX

NAME

ADDRESS

PHONE   FAX

NAME

ADDRESS

PHONE   FAX

NAME

ADDRESS

PHONE   FAX

NAME

ADDRESS

PHONE   FAX

NAME

ADDRESS

PHONE   FAX

NAME

ADDRESS

PHONE   FAX

NAME

ADDRESS

PHONE   FAX

NAME

ADDRESS

PHONE   FAX

NAME

ADDRESS

PHONE   FAX

NAME

ADDRESS

PHONE   FAX

NAME

ADDRESS

PHONE   FAX

NAME

ADDRESS

PHONE   FAX

V

NAME

ADDRESS

PHONE   FAX

NAME

ADDRESS

PHONE   FAX

NAME

ADDRESS

PHONE   FAX

NAME

ADDRESS

PHONE   FAX

NAME

ADDRESS

PHONE   FAX

NAME

ADDRESS

PHONE   FAX

NAME

ADDRESS

PHONE   FAX

BEARDED IRIS

NAME

ADDRESS

PHONE   FAX

NAME

ADDRESS

PHONE   FAX

NAME

ADDRESS

PHONE   FAX

NAME

ADDRESS

PHONE   FAX

NAME

ADDRESS

PHONE   FAX

NAME

ADDRESS

PHONE   FAX

NAME

ADDRESS

PHONE   FAX

NAME

ADDRESS

PHONE   FAX

NAME

ADDRESS

PHONE   FAX

NAME

ADDRESS

PHONE   FAX

NAME

ADDRESS

PHONE   FAX

NAME

ADDRESS

PHONE   FAX

NAME

ADDRESS

PHONE   FAX

NAME

ADDRESS

PHONE   FAX

WX

NAME

ADDRESS

PHONE   FAX

NAME

ADDRESS

PHONE   FAX

NAME

ADDRESS

PHONE   FAX

NAME

ADDRESS

PHONE   FAX

NAME

ADDRESS

PHONE   FAX

NAME

ADDRESS

PHONE   FAX

NAME

ADDRESS

PHONE   FAX

CHAENOMELES SPECIOSA 'NIVALIS'

NAME

ADDRESS

PHONE   FAX

NAME

ADDRESS

PHONE   FAX

NAME

ADDRESS

PHONE   FAX

NAME

ADDRESS

PHONE   FAX

NAME

ADDRESS

PHONE   FAX

NAME

ADDRESS

PHONE   FAX

NAME

ADDRESS

PHONE   FAX

NAME

ADDRESS

PHONE   FAX

NAME

ADDRESS

PHONE   FAX

NAME

ADDRESS

PHONE   FAX

NAME

ADDRESS

PHONE   FAX

NAME

ADDRESS

PHONE   FAX

NAME

ADDRESS

PHONE   FAX

NAME

ADDRESS

PHONE   FAX

YZ

NAME

ADDRESS

PHONE   FAX

NAME

ADDRESS

PHONE   FAX

NAME

ADDRESS

PHONE   FAX

NAME

ADDRESS

PHONE   FAX

NAME

ADDRESS

PHONE   FAX

NAME

ADDRESS

PHONE   FAX

NAME

ADDRESS

PHONE   FAX